Lolita's Family

Written by Elena Castro, Barbara Flores, and Eddie Hernández
Illustrated by Raúl Espinoza

D1537462

Celebration Press

An Imprint of Addison-Wesley Educational Publishers, Inc.

My family and I are farmworkers.

On Monday we go to a farm.

On Tuesday we pick red strawberries.

On Wednesday we pick purple grapes.

On Thursday we pick green lettuce.

On Friday we pick white onions.

On Saturday we rest.